AMERICAN ELVES - THE YANKOOS

THE YANKOOS

AND

THE OAK-HICKORY FOREST ECOLOGY

BOOK TWO

By Robert Frieders, Ph.D.

One of a Yankoo Series of Books

Yankoo Publishing Co.

AMERICAN ELVES - THE YANKOOS

THE YANKOOS

AND

THE OAK-HICKORY FOREST ECOLOGY

BOOK TWO

By Robert Frieders, Ph.D.

One of a Yankoo Series of Books

Published by: Yankoo Publishing Co.
10616 Cameo Drive
Sun City, Arizona 85351

Copyright   1993 by Robert Frieders

First Printing 1994

Printed in the United States of America

Library of Congress Catalog Card Number 93-61530

ISBN 0-9639284-1-4   Soft cover 6x9

Acknowledgments

Many fine people have contributed with their talents in the effort that has made this book a reality.

The author is especially indebted to his wife, Dottie, for her encouragement, as well as constructive observations as the manuscript was taking shape. Dottie has spent many hours in the forest taking yankoo and nature pictures.

Dr. Mamie Ross, a reading specialist, and her husband, Jim, have helped with their observations as the manuscript was being written. Dr. Ross has served as a consultant.

Professor Marge Edwards has helped edit the manuscript. Professor Edwards, in work at the college and university level, has demonstrated her mastery of the English language.

Lorraine Glicksman, my niece, has used her typing and computer talents in preparing the manuscript for the printer.

Elliot Glicksman, Lorraine's husband, has provided invaluable help with legal aspects regarding copyright and trademark matters.

Burley Packwood, a neighbor in Sun City, having published three books of his own, was able to give the author valuable information on how to proceed with a manuscript in having it printed.

Paul and Norma Frieders, and Gloria Jean Noble, my niece, have also been helpful to the author as the manuscript was written.

Then there are two longtime friends who helped with their Irish observations as the manuscript was taking form; Sr. Mary Charlotte Kavanaugh, O.S.B., and Sr. Bernice Kavanaugh, O.S.B.

Many thanks to all of these people. They have played an important role in the development of this Yankoo book. We are all proud to present the Yankoos, American Elves, in nature's forest setting.

Coming Of The Leaves Spring Festival

In early spring, the trees of the Oak-Hickory Forest once again bring forth leaves. With the coming of leaves, all life in the forest begins a new year of activity. The yankoos, American elves, celebrate this event with a spring festival. The reader will meet the yankoos pictured at the festival on these two pages, in the yankoo series of books.

Besides commenting on yankoo life, these fascinating yankoos will point out to the reader some of the wonderful aspects of life in a forest. How the plants and the animals interact with one another and with the environment will be shown. A reader should gain a new appreciation of one part of our national heritage - the plants and animals of a forest. Such a natural treasure should be carefully protected and handed on intact to the Americans of the future.

Table of Contents

CHAPTER ONE

LESTER - ON HIS MAIL ROUTE

Lester is going through the patch of ginger plants on his way to the house of Ichabod, the yankoo fisherman.

Hello, my friend!
I am Lester, the yankoo mailman.
Come with me on my mail route. We will
deliver the letters together. You will meet some
forest yankoos. Along the way, you will also learn
about many interesting forest plants and animals.

Let's see now....here in my mail pouch....what's the next letter?

Ah ha...here it is...the letter is for Ichabod, the fisherman.

I'll bet, my friend, that you can almost see him, can't you?

He would be sitting on the bank of a stream, wouldn't he? He would have his fishing pole, and he probably would be leaning back against a tree trunk. Yes, you have done a good job of imagining what Ichabod is doing.

Looking at him that way, one might think that Ichabod is lazy. One might think that he has an easy life. But, that is not the case. Our Ichabod is a very active yankoo. All the yankoos depend on Ichabod for their fish food. Ichabod is a very good fisherman. You will meet him later.

Now, let's turn here to the left.

See that patch of plants up ahead? Those plants are ginger plants.

All the yankoos learn in school about the ginger plant. They collect the roots of the plant. It makes a nice spice for some food. Bruno, the baker, makes gingerbread cookies and cakes. And Smiley makes his yankoo ginger ale from it.

GINGER PLANT
AND FLOWER

The ginger plant is a little plant. It grows near the ground. It has two large leaves. A purple colored flower grows up between the leaves. That flower, my friend, is nice looking. But, oh the terrible smell it makes. Not many things would come near a flower that smells like that.

However, not everything stays away from the smell. There is a fly that loves it. Once the fly smells the terrible odor, it flies to the flower.

It means food to the fly. It will drink the nectar of the flower. In securing the nectar, the fly pollinates the flower.

Once pollinated, the flower produces ginger plant seeds.

The seeds develop there on the flower stalk.

In our forest, we have many, many ants. Ants are curious insects. Ants look all over for food. They will find the ginger seeds.

Then, they carry the ginger seeds back to the ant nest.

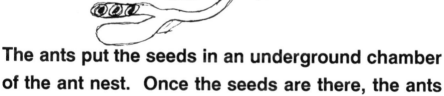

The ants put the seeds in an underground chamber of the ant nest. Once the seeds are there, the ants eat the outside covering of the ginger seeds.

The ginger seed covering is a tasty food for ants. The ants will only eat the seed coat. They do not eat the ginger seeds.

The ginger seed now has no seed coat. It can then sprout and make a small ginger plant.

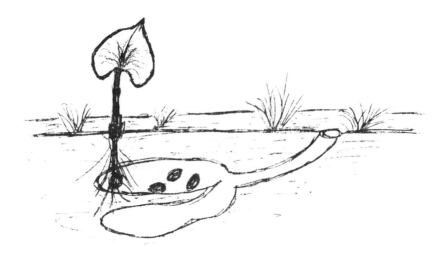

The first year the plant makes one leaf. This leaf makes food and grows in size. It also stores food in the stem and roots.

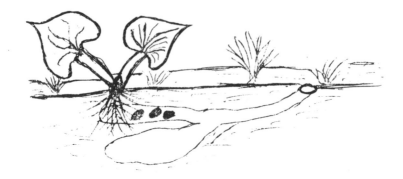

The next year the stored food in the stem and roots produces a ginger plant with two leaves. The plant will also make the ginger flower with its terrible odor.

My friend, you see how wonderful nature is. First,
the ginger plant needed the flies. It gave off that
terrible smell to draw the flies to it.

The flies helped make the seed. The flies received
the nectar food for helping make the seed.

Then the ants really loved the
outer coat of the seed. It was
a tasty food for them. They moved
the seed to a new spot. They did
not eat the seed but just the outer
coat. So now, for this food, the
ants have put the seed in a new place.

Now, it can sprout into a ginger plant in the old ant nest.

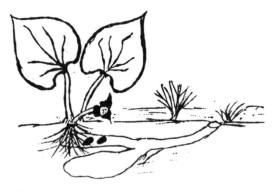

Thus, a new ginger plant starts growing in a new place. The forest animals, the flies, and ants have made this possible.

So it is in nature. All the different animals and plants need one another. Animals and plants of the forest are dependent on one another in order to live.

The same holds true, my friend, for the yankoos. All yankoos are dependent on one another.

You know, my friend, I found out how important this was. When I became the mailman, I realized it. The yankoos depended on me to deliver their mail. I just had to be dependable in my job.

The yankoos depend on other yankoos. Barnaby, the butcher, provides all yankoos with their meat food. Bruno, the baker, makes the bread, cookies, cakes, and pies for all yankoos. So the butcher, the baker, the schoolmaster, and others, are all needed.

The yankoos depend on these and other yankoos. It is very important that every yankoo be dependable. The yankoos rely on each yankoo. They expect each yankoo will do his part. Yankoo life is wonderful when every forest yankoo is dependable. It is the same, I am told, with the yankees. Every yankee in his life depends upon other yankees. Yankee life is wonderful when yankees are dependable.

Look up ahead there. Do you see that large tree? That is a sassafras tree. The sassafras tree is another tree growing in our forest. All trees make leaves. All the leaves of any tree are very much alike. That is all..except for the sassafras tree. The leaves of the sassafras tree take on various shapes. As you can see, all of those leaves were taken from one sassafras tree.

Notice one leaf has no indentation. Another leaf looks like a mitten. Others have three forks as it were.

My friend, look at this small sassafras tree over here. Notice the different shape leaves on this tree. There are some entire leaves. They have no indentations and are rather egg-shaped. Several of the leaves have a mitten and thumb shape. There are also a number of larger leaves that have a three-fingers outline. A sassafras tree, even when very small, has different shape leaves. In nature, it is rather unusual for a tree to have leaves of different shapes. As a rule, all leaves on any tree have the same basic shape. So, in this way, the sassafras is different from other trees.

That sassafras tree, my friend, is different also in another way. A new tree can start growing from a sassafras tree root. Not many trees can do this. Here, let me get out my sketch pad. I will make a sketch of it for you. Ah, here is my pad. Now, let me sketch it.

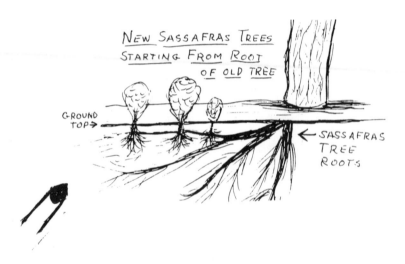

The large sassafras tree root is there underground. I have put in three new trees. They are all starting from that tree root. These new trees will grow fast. They use the food from the root of the big tree. Soon the new trees develop their own root system. Then, each breaks the connection with the big tree root. Each tree is now on its own. Thus, new sassafras trees have started from a tree root. In nature, there are not many trees that can do this.

Most trees reproduce by seeds. The sassafras tree also reproduces by seeds. Let me sketch a sassafras fruit for you.

There is a stem with some leaves. Notice the fruit stems. Each has a fruit on the end. It is a berry-like fruit. In fall, it becomes dark blue in color. Then, the fruit is mature. Inside each fruit is the sassafras seed. The wild turkeys of our forest like this fruit. When it is mature, they eat the fruit. Other birds of the forest also eat the fruit. Inside the bird's stomach, the fruit is digested. It is food for the bird. The seed inside the fruit is not digested. The seed is cast out in the bird dropping. So now a sassafras seed is in another spot in the forest. Given a little rain and good weather, the seed will sprout. The bird dropping is just like a little fertilizer. It will help it get a good start in life.

So you realize, my friend, the forest plants and animals need one another. Here the sassafras tree needed the turkeys and other birds. The turkeys and other birds needed the sassafras tree. The sassafras seed could not pick itself up and move to another spot. So the plant made a fruit, some food around the seed. The bird for this food moves the seed to a new place in the forest. That is the way in nature, my friend. Plants and animals of the forest need one another eventually to survive.

My friend, have you ever tasted sassafras tea? You haven't? Oh, you are missing a very tasty beverage. Sassafras tea is just delicious. Here, crush this leaf between your fingers. There, now, smell your fingers. It has a nice smell, doesn't it?

The leaves, bark, and roots have a sassafras oil in them. That is what you smell. It also makes a tasty tea for yankoos.

We collect roots from small trees. The roots are put in a pan of water. The mixture now stews for awhile. Then, one has a delicious tea. Sassafras tea!! Every yankoo likes the sassafras tea.

Every afternoon the yankoos get their tea break. Here, let me show you a section of our yankoo constitution. Here is the part about the tea break.

YANKOO CONSTITUTION

ARTICLE SEVEN:
EVERY YANKOO HAS THE INALIENABLE RIGHT TO ENJOY THE AFTERNOON TEA BREAK.

The yankoo constitution, in Article Seven, clearly states, "Every yankoo has the inalienable right to enjoy the afternoon tea break. Therefore, all yankoo work will stop at three o'clock. There shall be a half hour break." So you realize, my friend, in yankooland, the afternoon tea is sacred.

Every yankoo relaxes during this time and has his tea. Sassafras tea time has become a part of yankoo life.

Now, just ahead there, beyond that tree, we will find Ichabod's house.

Here is where we turn and head East, my friend.

See that tree over there? That is my marker. Notice that dome-shaped growth on the tree trunk. That is a burl. The tree grows faster in that burl area. So the fast growing tree material must "bump out" like that. Very few trees of the forest have burls. Usually, I see only one burl on a tree. Some trees, though, can have many burls.

Some of the burls become very large, several feet across. We have seen yankee lumbermen harvesting the large burls. I am told that burl wood makes beautiful yankee furniture.

There is Ichabod's house.

CHAPTER TWO

ICHABOD - THE YANKOO FISHERMAN

There is Ichabod, the fisherman. He is fishing by the stream that goes through the forest. Notice his fishing pole. He has caught a fish. The fish is bending the pole. Ichabod will give the fish "a little line," as they say. Then he will pull in his catch.

Ah, there is Ichabod. He has come out of his house to greet us.

"Salus, tibi tibi, Ichabod!" "Et tibi tibi, Lester!"

I had seen you by the large sassafras tree, Lester. So, I waited for you. Who is your friend, Lester?

Oh, my friend is going with me on the mail route. He wants to learn all about yankoos.

Glad to meet you. If you want
to learn more about us,
that's fine.
I am just getting ready
to head out and fish.
The pond is just up
ahead, Lester.

Why don't you come with me? I will show you many interesting things.

Well, Ichabod, we will go with you. Here, put your letter in the house. Get your fishing pole. We will wait for you.

All right, Lester, the letter goes into the house. Later, I will have time to read it. O.K., Lester and friend, let's go; time's a wasting.

See, my friend, there goes Ichabod. We will have to keep up with him. Once he has his fishing pole, off he goes to his pond.

See....the pond is just up ahead.

Here we are, my friend. This is our forest pond. It is a nice pond. I spend many hours here, fishing. All the yankoos depend on me to supply them with fish food. If I must say so, I am a good fisherman. I catch many fish for the yankoos.

My friend, this pond has so many interesting plants and animals. All one has to do to see them is to really look. One must observe carefully. Then, one sees many interesting things in nature.

Now, let me show you some animals living on top of the pond water. Yes...there are animals walking and dancing on top of the water. I see you smile at that, my friend. You find this hard to believe. I know, not many animals can walk on water. However, we have some here in our pond that do walk on top of the water.

Look over there by the bank, see that insect on the water?

See it go?

WATER   STRIDER   WATER

It's on top of the water.

It's so light that it just dimples the water surface with its feet. See those three pairs of legs?... Do you see them?... Well, the back pair of legs does the steering. The middle pair of legs pushes the water backwards. This moves the insect forward. The first pair of legs is held in front of the insect. They will grab any food in front of them.

See how fast they shoot about on top of the water?
They are called water striders. They walk on water.

These water striders are also acrobats. You know
what an acrobat is, don't you my friend? You don't
know? Well, let me tell you. An acrobat is one that
can jump up in the air and land on his feet. The real
acrobats make all kinds of fancy turns in the air, but
they still land on their feet. Well, these water
striders are real acrobats. They can jump up in the
air and land in another spot on their feet on the
water.

There, do you see what I mean? That pumpkinseed sunfish thought it had a tasty water strider. But the water strider saw the fish coming and "presto", it disappeared into the air. It jumped into the air. It landed on its feet. Now, it is some distance away from that fish. Living on top of the water can pose problems for the water striders. They must always watch out for the fish below in the water. If they aren't always careful, they could be food for a pond sunfish.

BLUEGILL
SUNFISH

PUMPKINSEED
SUNFISH

LOOKING FOR FOOD

Look over there. Do you see those bugs on the water surface? They are called the whirligig beetles. They waltz back and forth over the top of the water. They dance on top of the water.

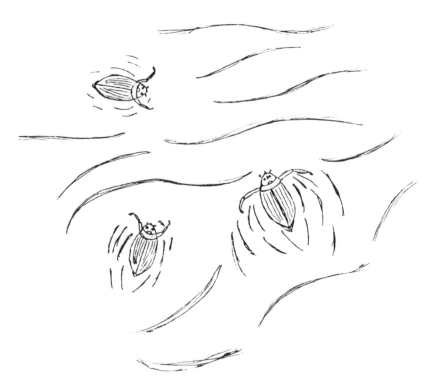

These beetles can also dive down into the water. They take a bubble of air down with them. They use the air in order to breathe. When they run out of air, they must come up to the water surface again.

The beetles eat animals and plants in the water.

These whirligig beetles can also produce a sound.

This is how they make a "squeak." They take the tip of their rear end and scrape it against their wing cover. This makes a nice "squeak."

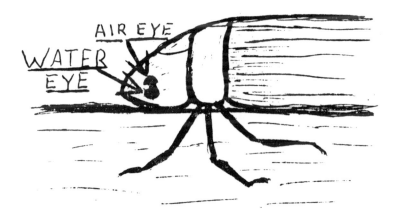

The whirligig beetle also has another unusual feature. It has two pairs of eyes. The upper pair of eyes sees what is in the air and the lower pair of eyes sees what is in the water. With this setup, no pumpkinseed sunfish will have it for a meal. Its water eyes will see the fish coming. It will waltz its way away to live another day.

Look at this insect
on the right. See
that speedster? That
is a back swimmer. It is
really swimming on its
back. In the water, it
looks like a boat that has
turned over, doesn't it?

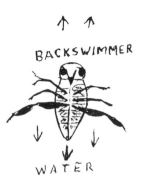

BACKSWIMMER

WATER

TAIL OPENING
ABOVE WATER -
WHEN IT NEEDS AIR

WATER

OAR LIKE
HIND LEGS

It can also swim on its stomach. It just turns over in
the water. Then, it is swimming on its stomach. The
back swimmer can also fly. It takes off right from
the water surface. "Presto", up it goes in the air.
Notice the pointed part between its eyes when it is
on its back. My friend, that nose-like thing comes to
a very sharp point. The back swimmer uses it to
pierce any animal which it has caught for food.

Now, let's observe other pond animals. Look over there by the shore. See that insect that has just taken off? That is a damsel fly. See it? It's not a strong flyer. It flutters along in the air.

Another damsel fly is sitting on that pond leaf. See it holding onto the leaf with its head up? The damsel flies are almost always found along the shore line.

Often, I see one damsel fly towing the other one. Look over there, my friend! There you see that very thing happening. One damsel fly is towing another. Notice the one doing the flying has grasped the one being towed just behind the head.

See that large insect? It's on that pond leaf. Do you see it? That large insect is a dragon fly. It's a dragon fly in the air around the pond. Notice it's much bigger than the damsel fly. This dragon fly can really fly!

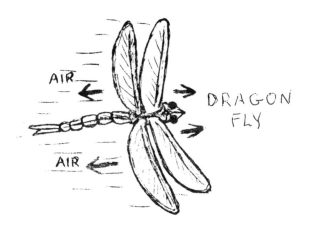

When it takes off, it goes! It's real fast; it's quick. It flies back and forth in the air around the pond. It can do something else, too. It can just stay in one place in the air without falling.

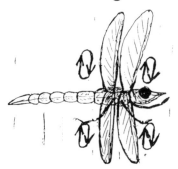

When an animal flies in the air and stays in one place for awhile without falling, we call that "hovering." We say that it "hovers." Now, "to hover," this dragon fly must beat its wings. It beats its wings, but it stays in the same place in the air..."it hovers."

There are many, many insects that live in and around the pond. The ones that fly in the air have to be very careful. When they fly, they must keep their eyes open for the dragon fly. If they are careless and don't watch, the dragon fly will swoop down on them. It will scoop them up. You see, the dragon fly's front legs form a basket. As it flies along, it scoops up this or that insect in its basket.

Then, it will go and rest on a plant. It will then eat the food it has caught.

There is a large dragon fly. It is on that leaf of that tree.

"Ichabod, look down there...
those leaves on the bottom
just moved. See, the leaves
just moved again. Do you
see it, my friend?" "We both
see it, Ichabod....it looks
like there are two eyes there."

"Oh yes, I see it now, Lester. Yes indeed, there is
something under those leaves. I think I know what
it is, too."

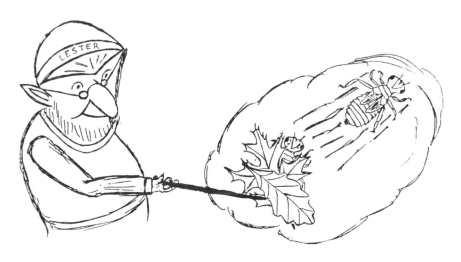

"Lester, touch those leaves with your stick... See
that dragon fly scoot out!!"

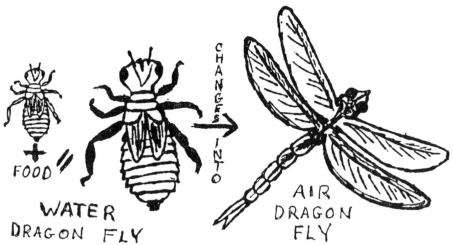

FOOD

WATER
DRAGON FLY

CHANGES INTO

AIR
DRAGON
FLY

Yes, that is a dragon, too, my friend. It hides under leaves and other things on the bottom. When another small animal comes by, it shoots out its jaws. Gotcha! Another insect is dragon food. Small insects in the pond try to be careful around this dragon. Of course, dragons also have to be careful. Fish love to eat these dragons. They are tasty morsels for fish. So...you realize....all the animals in the pond must be cautious. They could be food for another animal if they don't watch their step.

This dragon in the water catches insects. It grows larger. Soon it will crawl up on the plant leaf out of water. At last, it will turn into a real dragon fly. This is the early stage of a dragon fly's life. So it is a dragon as a youngster in the water. Then, it turns into a dragon fly - a dragon of the airways!

Look at this. Here is a big one, Lester and my friend. See that animal under that pin oak leaf? It is a really big one. It is the largest of all the insects in the pond. It is very much like the young dragon fly you just saw. It also hides under the leaves on the bottom of the pond. It waits for another insect to go by; then, it jumps forward. "Gotcha!" Another tasty bit of food for this bug. Oh, what's its name? Well, this insect is called the giant water bug. It is so much bigger than other water insects. I imagine they all look on it as a giant.

Give me your stick, Lester. I will make it leave its hiding place. Then you can see just what it looks like.

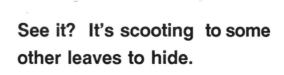

See it? It's scooting to some other leaves to hide.

Well, Ichabod, I believe that we will have to get along. There is much mail to be delivered. My friend and I will drop by in the afternoon. By that time, you will probably have caught a few fish. You can tell us all about it when we come by...so, "Salus, tibi, tibi, Ichabod." "Et tibi, tibi, Lester and my friend."

See, Ichabod has his can of worms with him. His hook is baited. Into the water, it goes. Ichabod is sitting there waiting for the big fish to take the bait.

Now, we must move on my friend. What was that?
Oh, you want to know about our greeting and saying
good bye? Well, let me explain it to you. Ichabod
and I always greet each other in the same way. I
would say, "Salus, tibi, tibi, Ichabod." That means,
"Health to you, to you, Ichabod." Those are some
Latin words. That's what they mean, "Health to you,
to you." Now, then, he would say, "Et tibi, tibi."
Those words mean, "And to you, to you." It's a nice
greeting - wishing one good health.

Salus, tibi, tibi.

Et tibi, tibi. You like that don't you my friend?
It is not only a nice greeting; it also has a nice
sound to it.

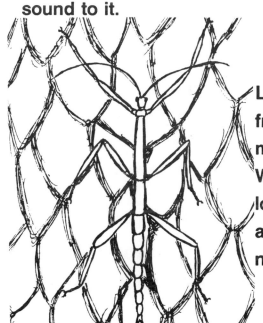

Look over there, my
friend. See that stick
moving? Well, that is a
Walkingstick insect. It
looks like a stick and
also walks. So the
name fits the insect.

Looking like a stick helps keep this insect alive. When a bird is near, the Walkingstick does not move. To the bird, it probably looks like another small twig of the tree. But if it moves, the bird would catch it. It would become a nice meal for a bird.

Walkingstick insects hatch from the eggs looking like the adults. The only difference is that they are very much smaller. Now, they eat leaves. In our forest, I have seen them eating oak leaves and Wild Cherry leaves.

That is quite an insect, isn't it, my friend. Well, we must be on our way. Our next stop will be at Lemonade Louie's house.

CHAPTER THREE

LESTER - ON HIS MAIL ROUTE

Lester on his route passes by this hollow log. His friend, the rabbit Jiminy, lives inside the log. It is his den and a place to hide when he is chased by the fox. All the yankoos are friends of Jiminy. One can often find Jiminy near one of the yankoo houses.

Now, let us go to the next yankoo house. Let me see... What is the next letter I must deliver? Ah... here it is.

See, it's a letter for Lemonade Louie. I wonder who is writing to Lemonade Louie. You know, the mailman likes to know where the letters come from. Oh, yes, I thought so. The letter to Lemonade Louie comes from Garry. Garry is a yankoo who lives in the Everglades. My friend, I notice that you laugh every time I mention Lemonade Louie's name. Well, I must admit, it is a funny name for a yankoo. But Louie has come by this name honestly.

It happened something like this. I just must tell you about it. Louie took a vacation a few years ago. He traveled down to the Everglades. Here...let me sketch it for you.

There is the Everglades.

The Everglades is a tropical swampy area.

Notice it covers the southern part of Florida.

There, Louie met Garry. Garry had come to America from the country of Wales. His name, Garry, in that country's language, means "gardener." Garry lives up to his name. He has what we call "a green thumb." Oh, that doesn't mean it's colored green. No. When we say one has a "green thumb", it means one has great success in growing plants. Garry lives near Everglades City.

Garry planted a few lemon seeds when he came over here from Wales. Now, those seeds have grown into very large lemon trees. Every year they produce many, many lemons.

Well, Garry made a lemonade drink from these lemons for Louie. Louie really liked that lemonade drink.

Louie Playing His Flute Under
Garry's Lemon Tree

Now you know here in the Oak-Hickory Forest we do not have lemon trees. No, they cannot grow here. The weather conditions here are not what a lemon tree needs. However, lemon trees really grow well down south in the Everglades. As you can see, this tree has made many lemons.

Louie, while down with Garry, fell in love with that lemonade drink. So, every year, Louie gets a yankoo wagonload of lemons from Garry.

YANKOO WAGON LOAD OF LEMONS

Everyday Louie has his lemonade. He drinks quite a bit of it...a yankoo wagonload of it every year. Well, you know what the other yankoos started saying? They said, "You know Louie has been drinking a few wagonloads of that lemonade the past few years."

With all that lemonade in him, there is more lemonade in Louie than there is Louie in him.

His name should really be 'Lemonade Louie'. And you know, my friend, to this day, he is known as Lemonade Louie to all the yankoos.

Look up ahead there. See the big billboard?

The Yankoo Trio has begun advertising for their spring music festival. Of course, our yankoo musicians will be the stars of the festival. Just wait until you hear the music of this Trio, my friend. I know you will enjoy it. All our yankoos just love to hear good music. I imagine that the Trio will be practicing for the event. They might be at Lemonade Louie's house. We shall see...

Before we go any further, I want to stop here. I am going to show you a real lion. Oh, it's not that large animal with big teeth that catches and eats other animals. No, it is not that lion. It is an ant lion. That's right, an ant lion.

It is a lion whose main food comes from the ants that it catches. Now, this ant lion doesn't run after the ants and capture them. No, this ant lion sets a trap for the ants. It catches the ants in a trap that it makes.

Here, let me get out my sketch pad again. I will draw this lion for you....

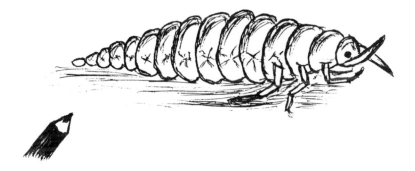

There, that is an ant lion. Notice the large sharp jaws.

Look, over there, my friend. Do you see those round pits on the ground?

Those are ant lion traps.

The ant lion is hidden down in the bottom of the pit.

Here, let me push aside part of the dirt.

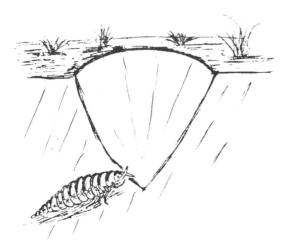

See, there is the ant lion. The ant lion makes the pit. Then it hides at the bottom of the pit, and it waits for an insect to fall into the trap.

You know, we have many ants in our forest. The ants are everywhere it seems. Well, the ants search for food on the ground here and there.

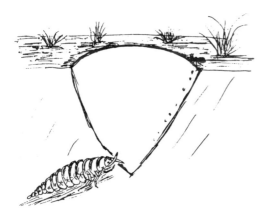

Eventually, an ant comes to the edge of the pit.

It leans over the edge.

It looks over the edge and knocks some sand grains into the pit.

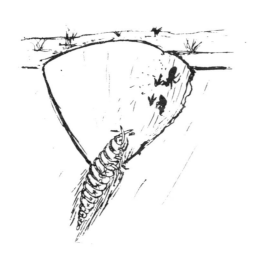

Immediately, the ant lion scoops sand from the wall where the ant is standing. The ground the ant is on now caves into the pit. The ant falls in. The ant lion throws sand at the ant.

The caved-in wall and the sand thrown by the ant lion bring the ant to the bottom of the trap.

The ant is now within reach of the ant lion.

The ant lion grabs the ant with its jaws. It makes a hole in the ant's body. It now shoots a secretion into the ant. This paralyzes the insect. Then, it sucks all the liquid out of the ant. Next, it tosses the dry carcass of the ant out of the pit. It then repairs the pit trap and waits for the next ant.

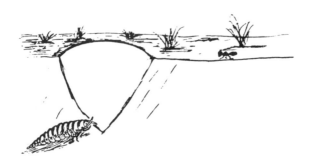

Many ants and other insects will fall into the ant lion's trap. With all that food, the ant lion grows bigger and bigger. Soon it is mature in size; it's as big as it will ever get.

Now, the ant lion spins a cocoon of silken threads around itself. It incorporates soil particles into the outermost layer.

Soon the thick silken cocoon is completed.

The ant lion is now inside this round silken cocoon.

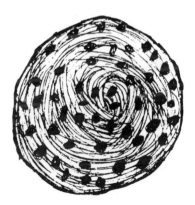

Great changes will take place inside the cocoon. The worm-like ant lion will change into an insect with wings. All this goes on inside the cocoon.

When all the changes have taken place, out will come the winged insect. It will chew almost a complete circle in the thick silken cocoon. Then it will crawl through the round opening to the outside. Left behind is the empty round silken cocoon with its hinged lid open.

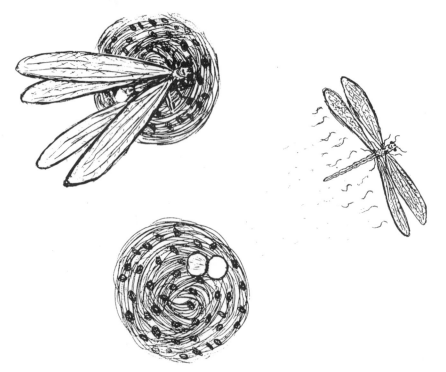

Then the winged insect will take to the air.

Soon these winged ant lions will mate. Then fertilized eggs will be dropped to the ground.

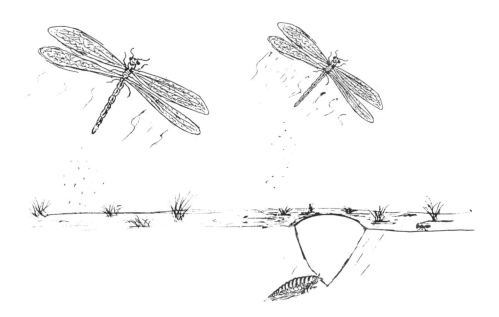

Each egg can develop into a very small worm-like ant lion. The small ant lion will then make an ant trap. Now, it is in business.

My friend, isn't that an interesting insect? Its life history is one of nature's wonders. The best of magicians could not change a worm-like creature into a flying insect. Only nature could do this.

My friend, there is a spider web over there.

The web is almost transparent. We have trouble seeing it. The flying insects don't see it either. That is all to the good for the spider that made the web.

I will put some arrows around the web. There are some web strands by the white arrows.

Now look at this picture. Lucky, the photographer, took this picture.

Isn't it beautiful? One can really see this wonderful spider web.

Spiders don't dig traps like the ant lion. Quite a few spiders make webs like this. They are traps in the air. Insects that do not see the web get caught.

Here the sun's early morning rays outline another spider web. An insect will fly by. By not seeing the fine threads, it will get caught in those sticky threads of the web. Once the insect gets caught, the spider

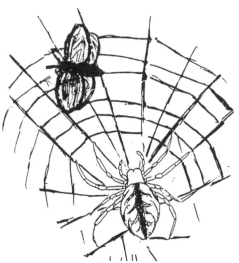

rushes to that spot. Many spiders then bite and paralyze the insect.

It now cuts the insect loose from the rest of the web. With its legs, it quickly turns the insect round and round. At the same time, it shoots out a liquid from its body at the insect. This liquid becomes a fine thread. This thread goes round and round the trapped insect. In essence, the spider quickly ties up the insect.

Then, the spider makes a hole in the insect's body. It now will pump out all the insect's body fluids. Just like the ant lion, it takes all the liquids out of the insect. Once it has done this, it lets the dry carcass fall to the ground. It will then repair the web where it had been torn in catching the insect. Once the web has been repaired, the spider will go again to the very center of the web. There, with its head down, it will now wait for another flying insect that gets caught in its web. That, my friend, is the way of life of this spider.

You wonder, how does this spider make such a wonderful web? Oh, it is a very fascinating process. I have watched this spider make its web many a day. It always follows the same procedure. It always makes the web in the same way.

All spiders making a web have body structures for making the threads of the web. The spider that makes this web has three pairs of spigots or faucets on its rear end.

Here, let me get out my sketch pad from my mail pouch. I will draw a few pictures to show you the steps a spider goes through in making a web like this.

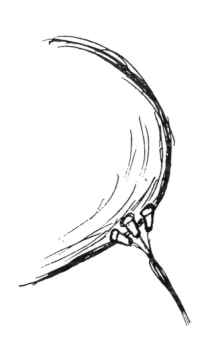

Here, I have drawn the spigots - three of them on the one side of the spider's rear end. When the spider shoots out a liquid through a spigot, it becomes a thread in the air. See, from the sketch, how the three spigots have shot out a liquid? The spigots are so arranged that several spigots can shoot out a liquid at the same time. See how the liquids all meet and form one thread in the sketch?

So, you see the spider has three pairs of spigots - six spigots in all. They are so arranged that liquid shot out from any number of spigots, all meet and form one thread. The spider can use these spigots to make strong threads used in the web framework. These are non-sticky. The spider can send out liquids from some spigots that make sticky threads. These are the threads where the flying insects get caught.

Let me draw a single spigot for you.

See the openings on that spigot are very, very small. One would almost need a microscope to see the openings in a spider's spigot. It is through these very small holes that the spider shoots out the liquids that make the web threads.

The spider has complete control over the kinds of threads it produces. Liquid from certain spigots turns into strong thick threads for the web framework. Liquid shot out of other spigots turns into the sticky threads that catch the insects.

Let's sketch the steps a spider goes through in making a web.

Let's say we have two trees with branches like this. Let's put the spider at A. This spider will now make a web between these two trees. First, the spider must make a thread bridging the space. It will be the A - B line on the drawing. The spider must first make this bridge thread.

There are two ways a spider could make the bridge thread. One way would be the following. The spider attaches a thread at A. Then it drops to the ground spinning a thread behind it. It then goes over to the second tree. It climbs up and out to the end of the branch at B. All the time it made this trip, it made a thread behind it. Now, it pulls in the extra line. Once it has a taut line to A, it cuts off the extra thread. Now, it attaches the end of the taut thread to B. Then the spider will go back and forth laying down more thread between A and B. This will make a firm bridge for the web.

Spiders also can make the bridge thread this way. Say the spider is at A on the sketch.

It raises its abdomen and points it toward point B. Then it shoots out a thread which is sticky on the end. A slight wind will help pull the thread toward B. Once the sticky end strikes the other branch, the bridge is made. This doesn't work on the first try all the time. The spider has learned to keep trying. Soon the sticky thread will stick to the branch. Once the free end sticks to the branch at point B, the bridge is made. Now, the spider attaches the thread

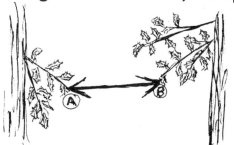

at A. Back and forth it goes laying down more thread. This makes for a firm bridge.

Then the spider glues a thread to one end of the bridge. It now goes across the bridge to the other end. This time as it goes, it spins out a thread that

loops down. On the other side, the spider attaches the end.

Now, it climbs down on this loop. The spider's weight brings it down. At the low point, it attaches a thread. Then it drops to the rock below spinning a thread. It now draws the thread taut and attaches the thread to the rock.

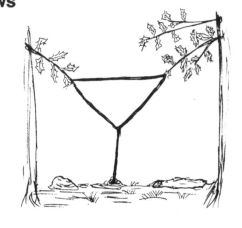

The spider climbs back up to a branch. It makes a strong thread and attaches it to the branch. Then it falls down to the ground spinning a strong thread as it goes. It then attaches the strong thread to that old branch lying on the ground. Next, the spider would climb up to the branch on the other side. It would do the same on this side.

It spins a strong thread and attaches it to the branch. Then, falling to the ground, it spins a strong thread after it. It attaches this to the rock there on the left side of my sketch.

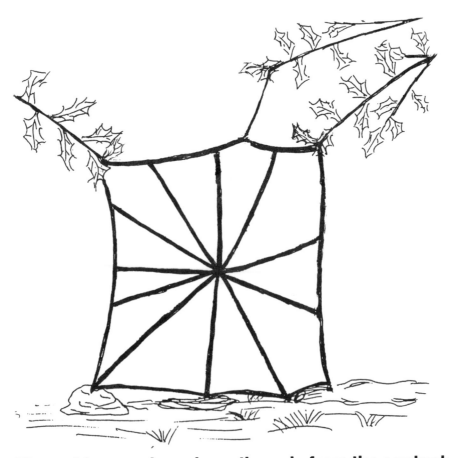

The spider now lays down threads from the center to the sides. The spider spins as much thread as it needs in making this framework. If it makes too much, it bites off what is not needed. So back and forth the spider goes making this framework. All of these threads are strong, non-sticky threads. These will be the main threads that the spider walks on when it moves over the web. Its eight legs will always be on these non-sticky strong threads of the web.

Next, it must firm up this framework. So the spider goes to the center of the web. Here, all the threads going to the sides are attached to one another. Now, it lays down a strong thread and attaches it to a side thread. It then proceeds in a circle making a strong thread. It attaches this to every side thread. It continues doing this while working towards the outside of the web. When it reaches a spot like that seen on the sketch, it stops making this circular strong thread. The web is now firm enough for the spider to add the final step in the web-making process.

The spider now makes the sticky threads of the web. These sticky threads will be the ones that catch the flying insects.

So, here I sketch the beginning of the work in attaching the sticky threads of the web. The spider now starts on the outer part of the web to lay down the sticky threads which it places close together. As it proceeds in a circular fashion, the web is becoming firmer. All these extra threads attached to the side threads make a strong web. It keeps going in a circular fashion laying down these sticky threads. At the same time that it cuts out the old non-sticky circular threads, it puts these sticky threads in the center of the web.

Here is a complete orb web. Soon, an insect will fly into the air trap the spider has set. You know, my friend, all spiders do us a great favor. They keep down the numbers of insects in nature. If it wasn't for the spiders, the birds, and other insect-eating animals, the balance of insects in the world would be upset. We would have too many insects. A fine balance now exists in our woods. We have enough insects for the woods' needs. But we don't have too many. Everything goes nicely in our woods when we have this balance. So the spiders do their part.

Did you hear that loud click, my friend? I thought you heard it. That insect over there made that sound. It is a Click Beetle. Sometimes it lands on its back when it is crawling around. Its feet cannot reach the ground when it is on its back. So it has to get back on its feet another way. Here, I will make some sketches for you.

Lying on its back, it bends its head and front end backward as in the drawing above. Then, suddenly it straightens out its body. This throws the beetle in the air. If it doesn't land on its feet, it will try again until it does.

We just have a very short distance to go to reach Lemonade Louie's house. Ah, there it is up ahead. It looks like the Trio is there.

CHAPTER FOUR

LEMONADE LOUIE, OSCAR AND HUBERT - THE YANKOO MUSICIANS

Lester is coming to Lemonade Louie's house. Lemonade Louie is playing his flute with his bowl of lemons and his other flute right in front of him.

Look, he has seen us...he is coming out of his house. There he is, waving to us. "Hi Lester! Glad to see you. Do you have a letter for me today?"

"Hi Lemonade Louie! Oh yes, there is a letter for you. It's from your friend in the Everglades. Here it is." "Thank you, Lester. Oh yes, it is from my friend, Garry. Who is your friend, Lester?" "Oh, this is a friend of Olaf's. He wants to learn more about the yankoos."

"Hello, my friend! I am glad you are going with Lester. If anyone knows about the yankoos, it's our mailman."

Lester, I guess you saw our sign back there on the path. You know, it won't be long before we will have our spring festival. My friend, we forest yankoos have two music festivals a year. One is held in the spring, and the other is held in the fall. All the forest yankoos come to our festival. The yankoos love our music - forest music.

I see that you have noticed my flute there in the bowl with the lemons. Yes, my friend, I play that flute. I must tell you something. After I have had some lemonade and start playing my flute, it just "comes alive" with those musical tunes.

What kind of music do we play, you ask? Well, the music we play fits in with the forest sounds.

We have some very talented musicians living here with us in our forest.

Do you see that bird over there on that branch of the oak tree? It is a gray bird with a black skull cap. That bird is a catbird. The catbird is a very versatile musician. It can sing the songs of almost all the birds of the forest. It is quite a copycat when it comes to singing. It can fool the best of the yankoo bird watchers. The song would almost make one believe that the other bird was present and singing it. But the catbird doesn't want to leave one under a false impression. Its song always ends with a nasal sound. The sound is something like the sound a cat would make. That sound has earned it the name -- catbird. In our forest, the catbird is just one of our many fine-feathered musicians.

In our yankoo music, we work in some of these musical bird calls. We pick up many of our "catchy tunes" from our feathered friends. At times, we also highlight some of the sounds of the forest insects. For example, the buzzing of the many bees, the katydid calls,

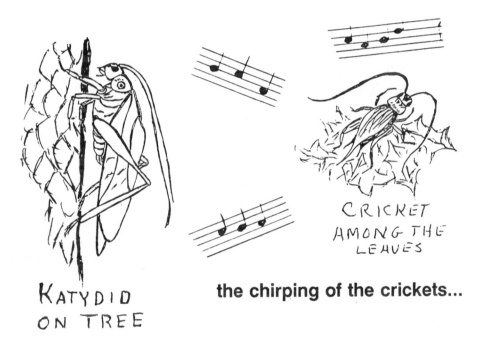

KATYDID ON TREE

CRICKET AMONG THE LEAVES

the chirping of the crickets...

all of these make beautiful forest music. Many of the forest insects provide us with added material for our musical pieces. So, you realize, my friend, that our yankoo music is a real reflection of the beautiful melodies heard daily in our forest.

Ah, here comes Oscar. Oscar is one of our musicians. "Oscar, we have a guest here. Would you tell him about the part you play in our Yankoo Trio?"

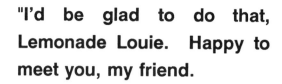

"I'd be glad to do that, Lemonade Louie. Happy to meet you, my friend.

Let me tell you what I do. See that stand over there, my friend?

I ring various bells in some of our musical pieces. Each bell is different in size, and each gives off a different sound when it vibrates."

The bell sounds are very clear sounds; they are happy sounds. We use the bells a lot in our spring festival. Our feathered friends, the birds, really sing in the springtime in our forest. One can just hear some bell tones in their calls.

Notice the row of boxes on the stand. These are wooden boxes that have sides, but no ends.

The boxes are all different sizes. When I strike the box with this soft mallet, the box vibrates producing a sound.

So each box produces a different sound. We yankoos use these boxes like you yankees use your drums. Playing on the boxes helps with our rhythm. My friend, we use those boxes in our "Woodpecker Serenade." It's a musical composition featuring our forest woodpeckers.

Let me first tell you about the woodpeckers that live in our forest. I have studied these wonderful birds. We have Downy Woodpeckers, Hairy Woodpeckers, Pileated Woodpeckers, Flickers, and Red-headed Woodpeckers in our Oak-Hickory Forest.

Look over there on that tree. Do you see that woodpecker? That is our Red-headed Woodpecker. Notice how it can hang there on the tree bark.

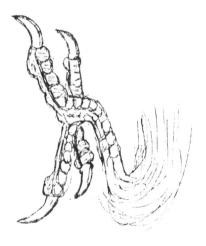

Each foot has two sharp claws pointed forward and two sharp claws pointed backward. The sharp claws dig into the bark and hold the woodpecker firmly to the tree trunk.

Woodpeckers look for insects on the bark of the forest trees. Notice how that Red-headed Woodpecker is going round the trunk, circling upward as it goes. The bird has caught an insect. That large beetle will soon be food for the woodpecker. They also make holes in a tree to catch insects that are living inside the tree. Some insects live in the wood of a tree. They eat the wood of a tree making tunnels in the wood an inch or so below the bark.

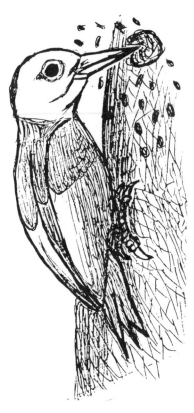

The woodpecker can hear the insects eating wood in those tunnels. Once it hears an insect at that point, it starts to make a hole there. The claws in the feet anchor it in the bark. Then the bird leans back on its tail for further support. The tail feathers of woodpeckers have strong central shafts. These feathers end in a rather pointed end to the shaft. So this also gives added support to the woodpecker. The beaks of woodpeckers are shaped like chisels. The beaks are mounted on skulls in a special manner. The muscles of the neck and head area are very strong.

So the woodpecker
starts to chisel
out a hole to
reach the insects.
The chips fly until
the insect
galleries or tunnels
are reached.

Then the woodpecker sticks its tongue into a tunnel.
It can change its short, wide tongue into a very thin,
long tongue. It can stretch the tongue a number
of times the length of its beak in this manner.

The tongue has backward pointed barbs on it. When it reaches an insect, it harpoons it.

Then it pulls its tongue out of the tunnel and swallows the insect.

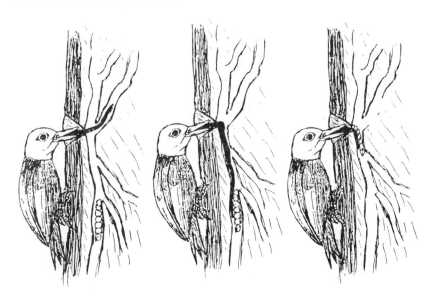

My friend, notice that tree over there. See the holes that the woodpeckers have made in the tree trunk. The woodpeckers probably found many insects there.

There I go again, Lemonade Louie - I get so interested in woodpeckers. They are just such wonderful birds. I want everyone to know about these birds. But...let's get back to music.

As I said, we have a piece we call the "Woodpecker Serenade." Into this musical piece, we have woven the songs of all the woodpeckers living in our forest. The Hairy Woodpecker, Red-headed Woodpecker, Downy Woodpecker, the Flicker, and the Pileated Woodpecker - the calls of all of these are used in this musical piece. In fact, we have even gone further than that. In the "Woodpecker Serenade," we have a musical sequence of woodpecker sounds making holes in trees. You might think that the sounds would be the same. But that is not so. A small woodpecker chipping away on a hole in a solid young tree produces one sound.

The large Pileated Woodpecker tearing up a rotten stump looking for insects produces a different sound.

And a Red-headed Woodpecker working on a hole in an older, partly-hollow tree, makes still another different sound.

In the springtime, the Red-headed Woodpecker sounds out. It beats rapidly on a selected branch which resonates. This is called drumming. The sound is amplified and made louder. This drumming is the way the Red-headed Woodpecker indicates its territory. The sound will be carried for a distance. No other Red-headed Woodpecker will come near the territory. If one does, the owner will drive it away. So we also have this drumming sound in our serenade.

I can create these sounds in our musical sequence with my boxes. We use our instruments in creating and developing our yankoo music. Our yankoo music, my friend, reflects the music heard daily in our forest.

"It's been nice visiting you, my friend. Now, I must go practice a dance routine with Hubert."   "Thank you, Oscar! I am sure we all appreciate your fine explanation."

"Well, there goes Oscar over to where Hubert is practicing. See, Hubert is over there, waving to us."

Hubert is the other member of our trio. He has been busy practicing on his harmonica. The piece he is practicing is very difficult. Much concentration and plenty of practice is the daily work of a musician. Oscar has now joined him. They will be practicing the "Yankoo Swirl." This is a new dance routine they have developed.

There they go on the "Yankoo Swirl."

Well, Lemonade Louie, we have learned a lot. I am sure my friend agrees with me. We will walk softly in the forest and be "all ears" as they say. You know, my friend, some yankoos joke about our big ears. Yes, big ears we do have. But our yankoo schoolmaster laughs at that. Listening is so important in life. You have those big ears to listen, listen, and listen.

"So we yankoos in the forest spend much time listening to what the forest tells us. Well, Lemonade Louie, good bye. We must be going."

Now, I must say "Good Bye" to you, my friend. In Book Three of American Elves - The Yankoos, I will continue on my mail route. I hope that you will come with me. We will be meeting Bruno, the yankoo baker. Bruno makes delicious cakes, pies, cookies, and other goodies.

Along our mail route we will see interesting forest plants and animals. We will meet Finian, the yankoo naturalist who is studying the butterflies of the forest.

Then we will deliver mail to Smiley and Reginald. They supply the yankoos with liquids - called "Smiley's Squeesins." Some of the "squeesins" are Big Pool Spring Water, Ginger Ale, Grape Juice, and Dandelion Wine.

So, I hope you will join us. Once again we will travel together on my mail route in Book Three. You will learn more about the yankoos and the plant and animal life of our forest.